Inner Reflections

2013 Engagement Calendar

SELECTIONS FROM THE WRITINGS OF
PARAMAHANSA YOGANANDA

 SELF-REALIZATION FELLOWSHIP

FRONT COVER:
Sunrise over Ullswater, Lake District, England
Photograph by Tom Mackie
Design by Shawn Freeman

NOTE: *Holidays and other observed dates are included for the United States (U.S.), Canada,*
England (Eng.), Wales, Scotland (Scot.), Australia (Aus.), and New Zealand (N.Z.).
In addition, moon phases and any eclipses are based on U.S.A. Pacific time.

Printed in Verona, Italy, by Studio Fasoli
4815-J2013

MIX
Paper from
responsible sources
FSC® C018568

*T*he scenery of mountains painted on the ever-changing azure canvas
of the sky, the mysterious mechanism of the human body, the rose, the
green grass carpet, the magnanimity of souls, the loftiness of minds,
the depth of love—all these things remind us of a God
who is beautiful and noble.

—*Paramahansa Yogananda*

THE PHOTOGRAPHS IN THIS CALENDAR are accompanied by selections from the writings of Paramahansa Yogananda, whose timeless and universal teachings have awakened many, of all races, cultures, and creeds, to a deeper awareness of the one reality that sustains and unites us all.

Whether spread over the vast heavens or hidden in the exquisite delicacy of a tiny flower, nature's beauty is always beckoning, inviting us to look behind the outward form and sense the presence of God within.

We hope that the thoughts and images in these pages will bring you inspiration and encouragement in the days and weeks of the coming year.

Sunrise over Ullswater, Lake District, England   Photograph by Tom Mackie

This is my New Year's wish for you:
that you all reach the land beyond your dreams,
where there is peace and joy eternal.

—*Paramahansa Yogananda*

Swans, Kushiro River, Japan   Photograph by Koji Okada/JTB Photo/SuperStock

December/January

31 monday

196th A 56th — 2:00 pm

1 tuesday

New Year's Day

2 wednesday

Day After New Year's Day (N.Z.)   Bank Holiday (Scot.)

3 thursday

4 friday

Last Quarter ◑

December 2012

s	m	t	w	t	f	s
						1
2	3	4	5	6	7	8
9	10	11	12	13	14	15
16	17	18	19	20	21	22
23 30	24 31	25	26	27	28	29

January

s	m	t	w	t	f	s
		1	2	3	4	5
6	7	8	9	10	11	12
13	14	15	16	17	18	19
20	21	22	23	24	25	26
27	28	29	30	31		

5 saturday

Paramahansa Yogananda's Birthday

6 sunday

January

7
monday

8
tuesday

9
wednesday

10
thursday

11
friday

New Moon ●

Dr. Sodhi - 11:15 AM

12
saturday

January

s	m	t	w	t	f	s
		1	2	3	4	5
6	7	8	9	10	11	12
13	14	15	16	17	18	19
20	21	22	23	24	25	26
27	28	29	30	31		

February

s	m	t	w	t	f	s
					1	2
3	4	5	6	7	8	9
10	11	12	13	14	15	16
17	18	19	20	21	22	23
24	25	26	27	28		

13
sunday

𝒜s the solid substance we call ice appears from water, steam,
or hydrogen-oxygen gas, so the solid earth with its oceans and vapors
appears out of the universe of Cosmic Energy.

—Paramahansa Yogananda

Helmcken Falls, British Columbia, Canada   Photograph by Adam Gibbs

Go to some peaceful place and stay alone for a while,
listening to the soft sounds of nature and of God within.

—*Paramahansa Yogananda*

Duck Mountain Provincial Park, Manitoba, Canada   Photograph by Mike Grandmaison

January

14
monday

1:30 - Dr. sodhi

15
tuesday

16
wednesday

17
thursday

18
friday

First Quarter ◗

January

s	m	t	w	t	f	s
		1	2	3	4	5
6	7	8	9	10	11	12
13	14	15	16	17	18	19
20	21	22	23	24	25	26
27	28	29	30	31		

19
saturday

February

s	m	t	w	t	f	s
					1	2
3	4	5	6	7	8	9
10	11	12	13	14	15	16
17	18	19	20	21	22	23
24	25	26	27	28		

20
sunday

January

21 monday

Habitude Phne # 782-2898 - BAIIARD
#299-0886 - Fremont

22 tuesday

23 wednesday

24 thursday

Hair cut - 12:45 - Cristy CARNER
Cristy ? - Fremont - Salon
Erica- Stylist - 548-8224

25 friday

26 saturday

Full Moon ○

27 sunday

	January					
s	m	t	w	t	f	s
		1	2	3	4	5
6	7	8	9	10	11	12
13	14	15	16	17	18	19
20	21	22	23	24	25	26
27	28	29	30	31		

	February					
s	m	t	w	t	f	s
					1	2
3	4	5	6	7	8	9
10	11	12	13	14	15	16
17	18	19	20	21	22	23
24	25	26	27	28		

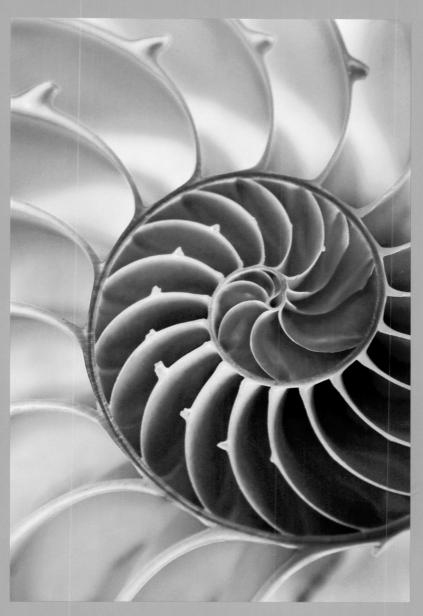

*I*t is so interesting to see the marvelous evolution of complex matter
from the singular consciousness of Spirit.
How intricate it is, and yet so simple.

—*Paramahansa Yogananda*

Nautilus shell, Alpharetta, Georgia   Photograph by Charles Needle

$\mathcal{F}$loat serenely on the waters of worldly life, ever intent on God.

—*Paramahansa Yogananda*

Spinecheek anemonefish, Papua New Guinea   Photograph by Mark Conlin/AnimalsAnimals

January/February

Australia Day (Aus. – Observed)

(12th)

28
monday

29
tuesday

Miele → WASH. → Repair
12:00 - 2:00 P.M.

30
wednesday

31
thursday

1
friday

January

s	m	t	w	t	f	s
		1	2	3	4	5
6	7	8	9	10	11	12
13	14	15	16	17	18	19
20	21	22	23	24	25	26
27	28	29	30	31		

2
saturday

February

s	m	t	w	t	f	s
					1	2
3	4	5	6	7	8	9
10	11	12	13	14	15	16
17	18	19	20	21	22	23
24	25	26	27	28		

Last Quarter ◑

3
sunday

February

4
monday

5
tuesday

6
wednesday

Waitangi Day (N.Z.)

7
thursday

8
friday

			February			
s	m	t	w	t	f	s
					1	2
3	4	5	6	7	8	9
10	11	12	13	14	15	16
17	18	19	20	21	22	23
24	25	26	27	28		

9
saturday

New Moon ●

			March			
s	m	t	w	t	f	s
					1	2
3	4	5	6	7	8	9
10	11	12	13	14	15	16
17	18	19	20	21	22	23
24 31	25	26	27	28	29	30

10
sunday

$\mathcal{W}$alk the pathway of life with God in your heart.

—*Paramahansa Yogananda*

Guanaco, Torres del Paine National Park, Patagonia, Chile   Photograph by Rosanne Tackaberry

$\mathcal{L}$ove cannot be had for the asking;
it comes only as a gift from the heart of another.

—*Paramahansa Yogananda*

Columbian ground squirrel, Banff National Park, Alberta, Canada   Photograph by Shaun Cunningham

February

11 monday

1-800-937-8997

12 tuesday

Lincoln's Birthday

13 wednesday

14 thursday

St. Valentine's Day (U.S., Canada, and U.K.)

15 friday

February

s	m	t	w	t	f	s
					1	2
3	4	5	6	7	8	9
10	11	12	13	14	15	16
17	18	19	20	21	22	23
24	25	26	27	28		

16 saturday

March

s	m	t	w	t	f	s
					1	2
3	4	5	6	7	8	9
10	11	12	13	14	15	16
17	18	19	20	21	22	23
24 31	25	26	27	28	29	30

First Quarter ◐

17 sunday

February

18
monday

19
tuesday

20
wednesday

21
thursday

1:30 — hair cut

Sew. Order
1000-3671-
6600-
2080

22
friday

Comcast — 244-0487

1-800 dede 2278

23
saturday

1-800-COMCAST

Opt #4 ➔

cancel

24
sunday

when get next Bill — wait 1-mo

+ call + cancel internet Serv —

Bill's (get to
39.00

February

s	m	t	w	t	f	s
					1	2
3	4	5	6	7	8	9
10	11	12	13	14	15	16
17	18	19	20	21	22	23
24	25	26	27	28		

March

s	m	t	w	t	f	s
					1	2
3	4	5	6	7	8	9
10	11	12	13	14	15	16
17	18	19	20	21	22	23
24 31	25	26	27	28	29	30

Seek quiet places where you can regularly get away by yourself
and be free to think of God.

—*Paramahansa Yogananda*

Fortress Mountain, Alberta, Canada   Photograph by Tim Fitzharris

*I*n the solitude of my inner silence
I have found the paradise of unending Joy.

—*Paramahansa Yogananda*

Palm tree, Virgin Islands National Park, St. John   Photograph by Dennis Frates

S

Full Moon ○

25
monday

26
tuesday

27
wednesday

28
thursday

✓

MASTERCARD - 1-8~~77~~-624-2768

St. David's Day (Wales)

1
friday

February						
s	m	t	w	t	f	s
					1	2
3	4	5	6	7	8	9
10	11	12	13	14	15	16
17	18	19	20	21	22	23
24	25	26	27	28		

1-800-325-5877

2 DVDS - 3 - DVD's

Joy of Juicing reversing arthritis naturally

2
saturday

Gary ~~Knotto~~ (Sp?) $180.—

Gary → reverse Arthritis + Pain naturally —

NULL

March						
s	m	t	w	t	f	s
					1	2
3	4	5	6	7	8	9
10	11	12	13	14	15	16
17	18	19	20	21	22	23
24 31	25	26	27	28	29	30

3
sunday

March

4
monday   *Last Quarter* ◑

5
tuesday

6
wednesday

7
thursday   *Paramahansa Yogananda's Mahasamadhi*

8
friday

			March			
s	m	t	w	t	f	s
					1	2
3	4	5	6	7	8	9
10	11	12	13	14	15	16
17	18	19	20	21	22	23
24/31	25	26	27	28	29	30

9
saturday   *Sri Yukteswar's Mahasamadhi*

			April			
s	m	t	w	t	f	s
	1	2	3	4	5	6
7	8	9	10	11	12	13
14	15	16	17	18	19	20
21	22	23	24	25	26	27
28	29	30				

10
sunday   *Daylight Saving Begins (U.S. and Canada)   Mothering Sunday (Eng.)*

$\mathcal{B}$e enthroned in the castle of goodness,
and your memories will be like beautiful flowers
in a garden of noble dreams.

—*Paramahansa Yogananda*

Crocus flowers, Vermont   Photograph by Warren Krupsaw

Surround yourself with the best company,
those who will inspire you
and strengthen your discrimination and will power.

—*Paramahansa Yogananda*

Schooling sweetlips fish, Indonesia   Photograph by Jones/Shimlock, Secret Sea Visions

11
monday

New Moon ●

12
tuesday

13
wednesday

NOON →

14
thursday

15
friday

March

s	m	t	w	t	f	s
					1	2
3	4	5	6	7	8	9
10	11	12	13	14	15	16
17	18	19	20	21	22	23
24/31	25	26	27	28	29	30

April

s	m	t	w	t	f	s
	1	2	3	4	5	6
7	8	9	10	11	12	13
14	15	16	17	18	19	20
21	22	23	24	25	26	27
28	29	30				

16
saturday

St. Patrick's Day

17
sunday

March

18
monday

19
tuesday   *First Quarter* ◐

20
wednesday   *Vernal Equinox*

21
thursday

22
friday

23
saturday

24
sunday

March

s	m	t	w	t	f	s
					1	2
3	4	5	6	7	8	9
10	11	12	13	14	15	16
17	18	19	20	21	22	23
24₃₁	25	26	27	28	29	30

April

s	m	t	w	t	f	s
	1	2	3	4	5	6
7	8	9	10	11	12	13
14	15	16	17	18	19	20
21	22	23	24	25	26	27
28	29	30				

$\mathcal{F}$ill your empty moments with love for God,
and you will know that you are not alone, nor can you be lonely.

—Paramahansa Yogananda

Arctic fox at sunset, Manitoba, Canada Photograph by Dennis Fast

$\mathcal{T}$he beauty of God is vast. To enjoy flowers for their loveliness is good, but far greater is to see behind their purity and beauty the face of God.

—*Paramahansa Yogananda*

Ranunculus flower, Oregon   Photograph by Dennis Frates

26
tuesday

First Day of Passover

27
wednesday

Full Moon ○

,30 days refund

28
thursday

A/104.90 - 1 can ⊃ - Cust Sev #
SmarT Medicine   1-866-219-
6371
#

29
friday

Good Friday

Supple - Powdered drink

March

s	m	t	w	t	f	s
					1	2
3	4	5	6	7	8	9
10	11	12	13	14	15	16
17	18	19	20	21	22	23
24,31	25	26	27	28	29	30

- Chondroitan - all US Based
USA - Glucosamine - DCE Bnt - Shell-fish
Free
Peter ApaTow

30
saturday

April

s	m	t	w	t	f	s
	1	2	3	4	5	6
7	8	9	10	11	12	13
14	15	16	17	18	19	20
21	22	23	24	25	26	27
28	29	30				

1-800-593-3490
Orange Powder
100 % money back

Daylight Saving Begins (U.K. and E.U.)   Easter Sunday

31
sunday

April

1
monday

Easter Monday (All except U.S. and Scot.)

2
tuesday

Last Quarter ◑

3
wednesday

4
thursday

5
friday

6
saturday

						April
s	m	t	w	t	f	s
	1	2	3	4	5	6
7	8	9	10	11	12	13
14	15	16	17	18	19	20
21	22	23	24	25	26	27
28	29	30				

7
sunday

						May
s	m	t	w	t	f	s
			1	2	3	4
5	6	7	8	9	10	11
12	13	14	15	16	17	18
19	20	21	22	23	24	25
26	27	28	29	30	31	

*T*hinkers do not accept the inevitable;
they turn their efforts toward changing it.
That is the ingredient that makes progress possible.

—*Paramahansa Yogananda*

Tawny owl, Bedfordshire, United Kingdom   Photograph by Brian Bevan/AnimalsAnimals

$\mathcal{T}$each me to feel Thy presence in me,
above me, beneath me, and around me.

—*Paramahansa Yogananda*

8
monday

9
tuesday

New Moon ●

10
wednesday

11
thursday

12
friday

April

s	m	t	w	t	f	s
	1	2	3	4	5	6
7	8	9	10	11	12	13
14	15	16	17	18	19	20
21	22	23	24	25	26	27
28	29	30				

13
saturday

May

s	m	t	w	t	f	s
			1	2	3	4
5	6	7	8	9	10	11
12	13	14	15	16	17	18
19	20	21	22	23	24	25
26	27	28	29	30	31	

14
sunday

April

15
monday

16
tuesday

17
wednesday

sprinkler Turned *on*

18
thursday

First Quarter ◑

19
friday

20
saturday

			April			
s	m	t	w	t	f	s
		1	2	3	4	5	6
7	8	9	10	11	12	13
14	15	16	17	18	19	20
21	22	23	24	25	26	27
28	29	30				

21
sunday

			May			
s	m	t	w	t	f	s
			1	2	3	4
5	6	7	8	9	10	11
12	13	14	15	16	17	18
19	20	21	22	23	24	25
26	27	28	29	30	31	

$\mathcal{Y}$oga is withdrawal of the attention from externals
in order to focus it on the inner source of Truth.

—*Paramahansa Yogananda*

Geranium flower, Maryland   Photograph by Craig Wood

$\mathcal{D}$elight in the vast play of life…God is joy and He created you in joy.

—*Paramahansa Yogananda*

Baby bobcat, Glacier National Park, Montana   Photograph by Larry Calof/AKM Images, Inc.

22
monday

Earth Day

23
tuesday

St. George's Day (Eng.)

24
wednesday

25
thursday

ANZAC Day (Aus. and N.Z.)   *Full Moon* ○

26
friday

April

s	m	t	w	t	f	s
	1	2	3	4	5	6
7	8	9	10	11	12	13
14	15	16	17	18	19	20
21	22	23	24	25	26	27
28	29	30				

27
saturday

May

s	m	t	w	t	f	s
			1	2	3	4
5	6	7	8	9	10	11
12	13	14	15	16	17	18
19	20	21	22	23	24	25
26	27	28	29	30	31	

28
sunday

April/May

29 monday

30 tuesday

1 wednesday

2 thursday

National Day of Prayer   *Last Quarter* ◑

3 friday

4 saturday

5 sunday

The kingdom of Bliss is spread tier upon tier unendingly,
beyond the blue vaults of heaven.
No matter how much joy you have,
look for more and you will get it....
March on endlessly in the eternal ether of meditation.

—*Paramahansa Yogananda*

Julian Alps, Slovenia   Photograph by Guy Edwardes

$\mathcal{B}$e kind to others
so that you may learn the secret art of being kind to yourself.

—Paramahansa Yogananda

Polar bear in fireweed, Hudson Bay, Manitoba, Canada   Photograph by Dennis Fast

May

6 monday

May Day Bank Holiday (U.K. and Scot.)

7 tuesday

8 wednesday

9 thursday

New Moon ●

12:15 - Cut Erica

10 friday

Sri Yukteswar's Birthday

May

s	m	t	w	t	f	s
				1	2	3	4
5	6	7	8	9	10	11
12	13	14	15	16	17	18
19	20	21	22	23	24	25
26	27	28	29	30	31	

June

s	m	t	w	t	f	s
						1
2	3	4	5	6	7	8
9	10	11	12	13	14	15
16	17	18	19	20	21	22
23 30	24	25	26	27	28	29

11 saturday

Mother's Day (U.S., Canada, Aus., and N.Z.)

12 sunday

$489.00   98026

May 8, 26 - 217 ST. S.W. Edmonds

13 monday
220th ST. Exit → WEST - Right-turn
ON 84th Avenu - ~~Test~~ Left on 216th ST S.W. -

Left 86th place WEST -
~~Back Right~~ hand cornE ⟺ 5 corners

14 tuesday
far Left ✓ of culdesAc

15 wednesday
Infront of The Bench
afternoon all me ("

16 thursday

17 friday

18 saturday

			May			
s	m	t	w	t	f	s
				1	2	3	4
5	6	7	8	9	10	11
12	13	14	15	16	17	18
19	20	21	22	23	24	25
26	27	28	29	30	31	

19 sunday

			June			
s	m	t	w	t	f	s
						1
2	3	4	5	6	7	8
9	10	11	12	13	14	15
16	17	18	19	20	21	22
23 30	24	25	26	27	28	29

𝒲alk surely on the garden path of life that leads to God.

—Paramahansa Yogananda

Keukenhof Garden, Holland   Photograph by Charles Needle

$\mathcal{R}$emain peaceful under all circumstances,
and let your peace "plant" blossom forth into flowers of smiles.

—*Paramahansa Yogananda*

Mexican poppy, Arizona   Photograph by Don Grall

May

20
monday

Victoria Day (Canada)

21
tuesday

22
wednesday

23
thursday

24
friday

Full Moon ○

May

s	m	t	w	t	f	s
			1	2	3	4
5	6	7	8	9	10	11
12	13	14	15	16	17	18
19	20	21	22	23	24	25
26	27	28	29	30	31	

25
saturday

June

s	m	t	w	t	f	s
						1
2	3	4	5	6	7	8
9	10	11	12	13	14	15
16	17	18	19	20	21	22
23 30	24	25	26	27	28	29

26
sunday

May/June

27 monday

Memorial Day   Spring Bank Holiday (U.K. and Scot.)

28 tuesday

29 wednesday

30 thursday

31 friday

Last Quarter ◑

	May					
s	**m**	**t**	**w**	**t**	**f**	**s**
			1	2	3	4
5	6	7	8	9	10	11
12	13	14	15	16	17	18
19	20	21	22	23	24	25
26	27	28	29	30	31	

1 saturday

	June					
s	**m**	**t**	**w**	**t**	**f**	**s**
						1
2	3	4	5	6	7	8
9	10	11	12	13	14	15
16	17	18	19	20	21	22
23 30	24	25	26	27	28	29

2 sunday

$\mathcal{T}$he butterfly of the soul must be freed
to spread its wings of beautiful divine qualities....
To the last day of your life, be positive; try to be cheerful.

—Paramahansa Yogananda

Paper kite tropical butterfly   Photograph by Darrell Gulin/Science Faction/SuperStock

Stillness has many screens, so has realization many layers....
Peel them like onions, and God will be ever hiding
behind every layer of perception.

—Paramahansa Yogananda

Rainbow eucalyptus, Kauai, Hawaii   Photograph by Julie Eggers

June

3 monday

4 tuesday

Haircut 1:00PM - Mc Laughlin Salon - VILLAGE
Kimberly 282 - 7657

5 wednesday

6 thursday

7 friday

June

s	m	t	w	t	f	s
						1
2	3	4	5	6	7	8
9	10	11	12	13	14	15
16	17	18	19	20	21	22
23 30	24	25	26	27	28	29

1-SCRAM

8 saturday

New Moon ●

July

s	m	t	w	t	f	s
	1	2	3	4	5	6
7	8	9	10	11	12	13
14	15	16	17	18	19	20
21	22	23	24	25	26	27
28	29	30	31			

3-Scram

9 sunday

June

6-scram

10
monday

10·scram
Thru The 25th

11
tuesday

12
wednesday

13
thursday

14
friday

June						
s	m	t	w	t	f	s
						1
2	3	4	5	6	7	8
9	10	11	12	13	14	15
16	17	18	19	20	21	22
23 30	24	25	26	27	28	29

15
saturday

July						
s	m	t	w	t	f	s
	1	2	3	4	5	6
7	8	9	10	11	12	13
14	15	16	17	18	19	20
21	22	23	24	25	26	27
28	29	30	31			

16
sunday

Father's Day (U.S., Canada, and U.K.)   First Quarter ◐

Remember your eternal connection
with the ever watchful Heavenly Father, God.

—*Paramahansa Yogananda*

Blacktail mule deer, Washington   Photograph by Shaun Cunningham

With the dawn of divine experience, with the dawn of divine joy,
we behold the glimmer of beautiful thoughts and experiences within our heart.

—*Paramahansa Yogananda*

June

17
monday

18
tuesday

19
wednesday

Summer Solstice

20
thursday

21
friday

June

s	m	t	w	t	f	s
						1
2	3	4	5	6	7	8
9	10	11	12	13	14	15
16	17	18	19	20	21	22
23 30	24	25	26	27	28	29

22
saturday

July

s	m	t	w	t	f	s
	1	2	3	4	5	6
7	8	9	10	11	12	13
14	15	16	17	18	19	20
21	22	23	24	25	26	27
28	29	30	31			

Full Moon ○

23
sunday

June

24 monday
OIL CHANGE
~~1:30~~ →

25 tuesday

26 wednesday

27 thursday

28 friday

29 saturday

Last Quarter ◑

30 sunday

I am Thy babe of eternity, safe in the cradle of Thine omnipresent bosom.

—*Paramahansa Yogananda*

Red fox kit, Manitoba, Canada   Photograph by Dennis Fast

*T*here is no end to your consciousness;
all things are glittering like stars in the firmament of your being.

—*Paramahansa Yogananda*

Hoodoos, with shooting star, the Milky Way   Photograph by Bret Webster/Photo Researchers, Inc.

July

1
monday

Canada Day (Canada)

2
tuesday

Hair cut 11:00 Am

3
wednesday

4
thursday

Independence Day

5
friday

July

s	m	t	w	t	f	s
	1	2	3	4	5	6
7	8	9	10	11	12	13
14	15	16	17	18	19	20
21	22	23	24	25	26	27
28	29	30	31			

August

s	m	t	w	t	f	s
				1	2	3
4	5	6	7	8	9	10
11	12	13	14	15	16	17
18	19	20	21	22	23	24
25	26	27	28	29	30	31

6
saturday

7
sunday

July

8
monday

9
tuesday

10
wednesday

11
thursday

12
friday

July

s	m	t	w	t	f	s
		1	2	3	4	5	6
7	8	9	10	11	12	13
14	15	16	17	18	19	20
21	22	23	24	25	26	27
28	29	30	31			

13
saturday

August

s	m	t	w	t	f	s
				1	2	3
4	5	6	7	8	9	10
11	12	13	14	15	16	17
18	19	20	21	22	23	24
25	26	27	28	29	30	31

14
sunday

$\mathcal{G}$od is the Cosmic Fountainhead of limitless Love.

—*Paramahansa Yogananda*

Fly Geyser, Nevada   Photograph by Ellen Anon

$\mathcal{F}$ree the mind from all disturbing thoughts and fill it with love and joy.

—*Paramahansa Yogananda*

$\mathcal{G}$od is the Master Painter.
His infinite beauty is suggested in the beauty of the flower.

—*Paramahansa Yogananda*

Pride of Madeira, Big Sur, California   Photograph by Terry Donnelly

*T*he cultivation of intuitive calmness requires unfoldment of the inner life....
Meditation is the way.

—*Paramahansa Yogananda*

Tropical lily pads, Oregon   Photograph by Dennis Frates

July/August

29 monday

Last Quarter ◗

30 tuesday

31 wednesday

1 thursday

2 friday

July

s	m	t	w	t	f	s
	1	2	3	4	5	6
7	8	9	10	11	12	13
14	15	16	17	18	19	20
21	22	23	24	25	26	27
28	29	30	31			

3 saturday

August

s	m	t	w	t	f	s
				1	2	3
4	5	6	7	8	9	10
11	12	13	14	15	16	17
18	19	20	21	22	23	24
25	26	27	28	29	30	31

4 sunday

8:45 / 1 1/2 hr. / L.Y. net / #20

5 monday

Hawaiian - Redemption #   Points →
1-888-267-2673 ←→   # #419,146 →

6 tuesday

Oct 4th - 9th coming P.M.   CLARK - G.D.
A.M.   # 194-B7
NON STOP - TO MAUI -

New Moon ●

7 wednesday

E - Decicio @ G. MAIL   3606 - WOODLAND PRK,
.com   AVE. N.
#311-98103
533 -   (206)   229-7331
88-4933)

8 thursday

Hawaiian Airlines Phone #
1-877-426-4537
My : Hawaiian - Member # → # 169-160-020

9 friday

Dept. # 2 Flight Jarny. -   Sear #
OCT. 4th - Fri: 10:05 AM arn. Maui - 1:05 P.M.   36C
Oct. 9th - 30   Lv maui - 2:14PM - arn: Sea: 11:05 P.M.   34G ← Seat #

10 saturday

Points : # 15,000   ✓ Baggage - 1 carryon Personals
666,651   25.00 is
35.00 35 - NOT 50 lbs
62" →
2 hrs - 30 mins →   Dr. License

11 sunday

CONFIRMATION # → # NQYZAZ
CODE   #
30.   40000 →   24hrs.

$\mathcal{T}$ranquility is the nature of God.

—*Paramahansa Yogananda*

VanDusen Gardens, British Columbia, Canada   Photograph by Adam Gibbs

 s the thread is hidden behind the beads of a necklace,
and as the dreamer's consciousness is secreted behind the garlands of dream images,
so the Divine Coordinator remains unseen behind the dream lei of creation....
It is God's consciousness alone that sustains all the dream appearance of creation.

—*Paramahansa Yogananda*

Water drops on spider web, British Columbia, Canada   Photograph by Adam Gibbs

August

12
monday

13
tuesday

First Quarter ◑

14
wednesday

15
thursday

16
friday

August

s	m	t	w	t	f	s
				1	2	3
4	5	6	7	8	9	10
11	12	13	14	15	16	17
18	19	20	21	22	23	24
25	26	27	28	29	30	31

17
saturday

September

s	m	t	w	t	f	s
1	2	3	4	5	6	7
8	9	10	11	12	13	14
15	16	17	18	19	20	21
22	23	24	25	26	27	28
29	30					

18
sunday

August

19
monday

20
tuesday

Full Moon ○

21
wednesday

22
thursday

Comcast Ser # 1-888-983-4369

23
friday

			August			
s	m	t	w	t	f	s
					1	2	3
4	5	6	7	8	9	10
11	12	13	14	15	16	17
18	19	20	21	22	23	24
25	26	27	28	29	30	31

24
saturday

			September			
s	m	t	w	t	f	s
1	2	3	4	5	6	7
8	9	10	11	12	13	14
15	16	17	18	19	20	21
22	23	24	25	26	27	28
29	30					

25
sunday

*A*waken the soul and remain ever wakeful,
striving each day to be different and better in all ways.

—Paramahansa Yogananda

Prairie dogs, Utah   Photograph by Dave Welling

$\mathcal{Y}$our heart is like the shore,
and the Ocean of Infinite Love is breaking on the shores of your heart.

—*Paramahansa Yogananda*

Foxglove, Oregon coast   Photograph by Dennis Frates

August/September

26 monday

Summer Bank Holiday (U.K. and Scot.)

27 tuesday

28 wednesday

Janmashtami   Last Quarter ◑

29 thursday

30 friday

Hab - # 762 - 2898
2nd - 297 - 0886

August

s	m	t	w	t	f	s
				1	2	3
4	5	6	7	8	9	10
11	12	13	14	15	16	17
18	19	20	21	22	23	24
25	26	27	28	29	30	31

September

s	m	t	w	t	f	s
1	2	3	4	5	6	7
8	9	10	11	12	13	14
15	16	17	18	19	20	21
22	23	24	25	26	27	28
29	30					

31 saturday

1 sunday

Father's Day (Aus. and N.Z.)

September

2
monday   *Labor Day (U.S. and Canada)*

3
tuesday

4
wednesday

5
thursday   *Rosh Hashanah   New Moon* ●

6
friday

			September			
s	**m**	**t**	**w**	**t**	**f**	**s**
1	2	3	4	5	6	7
8	9	10	11	12	13	14
15	16	17	18	19	20	21
22	23	24	25	26	27	28
29	30					

7
saturday

			October			
s	**m**	**t**	**w**	**t**	**f**	**s**
		1	2	3	4	5
6	7	8	9	10	11	12
13	14	15	16	17	18	19
20	21	22	23	24	25	26
27	28	29	30	31		

8
sunday

*I*nfinity is our Home.
We are just sojourning awhile in the caravanserai of the body.

—Paramahansa Yogananda

Zebra, Serengeti, Tanzania   Photograph by Jan Vermeer

*P*ractice meditation in the early morning....
The rays and vibrations of the dawn are vitalizing and spiritually uplifting.

—*Paramahansa Yogananda*

Seljalandsfoss waterfall, Iceland   Photograph by Tom Mackie

$\mathcal{M}$ost people are copies of someone else, imitating what others do....
You should be a different individual,
expressing the very best of your own unique nature.

—*Paramahansa Yogananda*

Western Columbine, British Columbia, Canada   Photograph by Michael Wheatley

When we awaken in God we shall realize that mortal life is only a picture made of shadows and light, cast on a cosmic movie screen.

—*Paramahansa Yogananda*

September

23
monday

24
tuesday

25
wednesday

Lahiri Mahasaya's Mahasamadhi   *Last Quarter* ◐

26
thursday

27
friday

September

s	m	t	w	t	f	s
1	2	3	4	5	6	7
8	9	10	11	12	13	14
15	16	17	18	19	20	21
22	23	24	25	26	27	28
29	30					

28
saturday

October

s	m	t	w	t	f	s
		1	2	3	4	5
6	7	8	9	10	11	12
13	14	15	16	17	18	19
20	21	22	23	24	25	26
27	28	29	30	31		

29
sunday

September/October

30
monday

Healthcare . Gov   Phone #
1-800 —

Lahiri Mahasaya's Birthday

only sites ending in . Gov .
no pre pay - for help choosing .

1
tuesday

Fine $95. — 1st yr.   Go on To State or Fed. Exchange
no response to Tex T, E-mails etc.

2
wednesday

~~1-855 Finder~~

3
thursday

4
friday

Hair Cut   782-2898
Shannon . O'Sullivan
Habitude - Fremont - 2:00

New Moon ●

	September					
s	m	t	w	t	f	s
1	2	3	4	5	6	7
8	9	10	11	12	13	14
15	16	17	18	19	20	21
22	23	24	25	26	27	28
29	30					

5
saturday

	October					
s	m	t	w	t	f	s
		1	2	3	4	5
6	7	8	9	10	11	12
13	14	15	16	17	18	19
20	21	22	23	24	25	26
27	28	29	30	31		

6
sunday

*G*od is not hiding from us.
He is speaking to us through flowers,
through our thoughts, through all creation.

—Paramahansa Yogananda

Three Sisters Wilderness, Oregon   Photograph by Kevin McNeal

In meditation…the power of God begins to reflect
in the clear waters of your consciousness.

—*Paramahansa Yogananda*

Autumn reflections, Strafford, New Hampshire   Photograph by Jane Wingate

7
monday

8
tuesday

9
wednesday

10
thursday

11
friday

First Quarter ◐

October

s	m	t	w	t	f	s
			1	2	3	4	5
6	7	8	9	10	11	12
13	14	15	16	17	18	19
20	21	22	23	24	25	26
27	28	29	30	31		

November

s	m	t	w	t	f	s
					1	2
3	4	5	6	7	8	9
10	11	12	13	14	15	16
17	18	19	20	21	22	23
24	25	26	27	28	29	30

12
saturday

13
sunday

October

14
monday

Columbus Day   Thanksgiving Day (Canada)

15
tuesday

16
wednesday

17
thursday

18
friday

Full Moon ○

October

s	m	t	w	t	f	s
		1	2	3	4	5
6	7	8	9	10	11	12
13	14	15	16	17	18	19
20	21	22	23	24	25	26
27	28	29	30	31		

19
saturday

November

s	m	t	w	t	f	s
					1	2
3	4	5	6	7	8	9
10	11	12	13	14	15	16
17	18	19	20	21	22	23
24	25	26	27	28	29	30

20
sunday

$\mathcal{S}$ilently and surely, as you walk on the path of life,
you must come to the realization that God is the only object,
the only goal that will satisfy you.

—*Paramahansa Yogananda*

$\mathcal{G}$od is the mirror of silence in which all creation is reflected.

—*Paramahansa Yogananda*

Grand Teton National Park, Wyoming   Photograph by Russ Burden

Your
2014 INNER REFLECTIONS
ENGAGEMENT CALENDAR
is now available in bookstores.

You may also place your order directly from Self-Realization Fellowship
by calling 818-549-5151 Monday–Friday from 9:00 a.m. to 5:00 p.m. Pacific time
or order online at:
http://bookstore.yogananda-srf.org

If you would like a free copy of Self-Realization Fellowship's complete
catalog of books and recordings, please request it by phone or
fill out the form below and fax or mail it to:

Self-Realization Fellowship
3880 San Rafael Ave.
Los Angeles, CA 90065-3219 U.S.A.
Fax: 800-801-1952

Name: _____

Address: _____

City:_____ State:_____

Zip code:_____

Daytime phone:_____ Date: _____

21
monday

22
tuesday

23
wednesday

24
thursday

25
friday

October

s	m	t	w	t	f	s
		1	2	3	4	5
6	7	8	9	10	11	12
13	14	15	16	17	18	19
20	21	22	23	24	25	26
27	28	29	30	31		

Last Quarter ◗

26
saturday

November

s	m	t	w	t	f	s
					1	2
3	4	5	6	7	8	9
10	11	12	13	14	15	16
17	18	19	20	21	22	23
24	25	26	27	28	29	30

Daylight Saving Ends (U.K. and E.U.)

27
sunday

October/November

28
monday

29
tuesday

30
wednesday

31
thursday
Halloween (U.S., Canada, and U.K.)

1
friday

		October				
s	m	t	w	t	f	s
		1	2	3	4	5
6	7	8	9	10	11	12
13	14	15	16	17	18	19
20	21	22	23	24	25	26
27	28	29	30	31		

2
saturday

		November				
s	m	t	w	t	f	s
					1	2
3	4	5	6	7	8	9
10	11	12	13	14	15	16
17	18	19	20	21	22	23
24	25	26	27	28	29	30

3
sunday
Daylight Saving Ends (U.S. and Canada)   New Moon ●

If we are attuned to God, our perception is limitless,
pervading everywhere in the oceanic flow of the Divine Presence.

—*Paramahansa Yogananda*

Sunset, White Sands, New Mexico   Photograph by Reed Nelson

$\mathscr{Y}$our role, however small, is just as important as the biggest
in contributing to the success of the entire drama of souls
on the stage of creation.

—*Paramahansa Yogananda*

November

4
monday

5
tuesday

General Election Day   Guy Fawkes Day (Eng.)

6
wednesday

7
thursday

8
friday

November

s	m	t	w	t	f	s
					1	2
3	4	5	6	7	8	9
10	11	12	13	14	15	16
17	18	19	20	21	22	23
24	25	26	27	28	29	30

First Quarter ◗

9
saturday

December

s	m	t	w	t	f	s
1	2	3	4	5	6	7
8	9	10	11	12	13	14
15	16	17	18	19	20	21
22	23	24	25	26	27	28
29	30	31				

Remembrance Sunday (U.K.)

10
sunday

November

11
monday

Haircut - NOON - Fremont - Shannon
782-2898

12
tuesday

13
wednesday

14
thursday

15
friday

	November					
s	m	t	w	t	f	s
					1	2
3	4	5	6	7	8	9
10	11	12	13	14	15	16
17	18	19	20	21	22	23
24	25	26	27	28	29	30

16
saturday

	December					
s	m	t	w	t	f	s
1	2	3	4	5	6	7
8	9	10	11	12	13	14
15	16	17	18	19	20	21
22	23	24	25	26	27	28
29	30	31				

17
sunday

Full Moon ○

𝒯race the visible effect to the Invisible Cause, the Spirit.

—*Paramahansa Yogananda*

Whenever you see a beautiful sunset, think to yourself:
"It is God's painting on the sky."

—*Paramahansa Yogananda*

Mount Seymour Provincial Park, British Columbia, Canada   Photograph by Michael Wheatley

Atty: John 5413 Meridian Ave N
675-0803

November

18 monday

19 tuesday

20 wednesday

21 thursday

22 friday

November

s	m	t	w	t	f	s
					1	2
3	4	5	6	7	8	9
10	11	12	13	14	15	16
17	18	19	20	21	22	23
24	25	26	27	28	29	30

December

s	m	t	w	t	f	s
1	2	3	4	5	6	7
8	9	10	11	12	13	14
15	16	17	18	19	20	21
22	23	24	25	26	27	28
29	30	31				

23 saturday

24 sunday

November/December

25
monday   *Last Quarter* ◑

26
tuesday

27
wednesday   *Hanukkah*

28
thursday   *Thanksgiving Day*

29
friday

November						
s	**m**	**t**	**w**	**t**	**f**	**s**
					1	2
3	4	5	6	7	8	9
10	11	12	13	14	15	16
17	18	19	20	21	22	23
24	25	26	27	28	29	30

30
saturday

December						
s	**m**	**t**	**w**	**t**	**f**	**s**
1	2	3	4	5	6	7
8	9	10	11	12	13	14
15	16	17	18	19	20	21
22	23	24	25	26	27	28
29	30	31				

1
sunday

$\mathcal{S}$eek that Divine Joy which gives meaning and purpose to life....
Plan your life: Map out the path of your desires
that they lead to peace-yielding, mind-satisfying goals.

—*Paramahansa Yogananda*

Railroad tracks, Vermont   Photograph by Kevin McNeal

𝒩ight was meant to screen all the attractions of the world,
that you might the more intently explore the kingdom of God.

—Paramahansa Yogananda

December

2
monday

3
tuesday

386 - 7387

386 - 7387

4
wednesday

5
thursday

6
friday

December

s	m	t	w	t	f	s
1	2	3	4	5	6	7
8	9	10	11	12	13	14
15	16	17	18	19	20	21
22	23	24	25	26	27	28
29	30	31				

7
saturday

January 2014

s	m	t	w	t	f	s
			1	2	3	4
5	6	7	8	9	10	11
12	13	14	15	16	17	18
19	20	21	22	23	24	25
26	27	28	29	30	31	

8
sunday

December

9
monday

First Quarter ◗

10
tuesday

11
wednesday

Take camos # 10 Shots — NOON - SIX — (12:00)

12
thursday

13
friday

Haircut — NOON - SHANNON

14
saturday

December						
s	m	t	w	t	f	s
1	2	3	4	5	6	7
8	9	10	11	12	13	14
15	16	17	18	19	20	21
22	23	24	25	26	27	28
29	30	31				

January 2014						
s	m	t	w	t	f	s
			1	2	3	4
5	6	7	8	9	10	11
12	13	14	15	16	17	18
19	20	21	22	23	24	25
26	27	28	29	30	31	

15
sunday

$\mathcal{R}$ealize that all the power you use—to think, to speak, and to act—
comes from God, and that He is with you now, guiding and inspiring you.
As soon as you actually realize that, a flash of illumination will come
and fear will leave you. Sometimes the power of God comes like an ocean
and surges through your being in great boundless waves,
sweeping away all obstacles.

—*Paramahansa Yogananda*

Gale-force winds driving waves, Sussex, United Kingdom   Photograph by Mary Clark/AnimalsAnimals

$\mathcal{E}$very day and minute and hour is a window through which you may see eternity.

—Paramahansa Yogananda

December

16
monday

Carin —
new transmission

17
tuesday

Full Moon ○

1:30   787-5565
rent a car —
pick-up —
2:00   economy

390. +TAX

$390.00   +TAX
40.00

$460.00

18
wednesday

19
thursday

20
friday

December

s	m	t	w	t	f	s
1	2	3	4	5	6	7
8	9	10	11	12	13	14
15	16	17	18	19	20	21
22	23	24	25	26	27	28
29	30	31				

January 2014

s	m	t	w	t	f	s
			1	2	3	4
5	6	7	8	9	10	11
12	13	14	15	16	17	18
19	20	21	22	23	24	25
26	27	28	29	30	31	

21
saturday

Winter Solstice

22
sunday

December

23
monday

24
tuesday

25
wednesday

Christmas Day   Last Quarter ◗

26
thursday

Boxing Day (Canada, U.K., Aus., and N.Z.)

27
friday

28
saturday

December

s	m	t	w	t	f	s
1	2	3	4	5	6	7
8	9	10	11	12	13	14
15	16	17	18	19	20	21
22	23	24	25	26	27	28
29	30	31				

January 2014

s	m	t	w	t	f	s
			1	2	3	4
5	6	7	8	9	10	11
12	13	14	15	16	17	18
19	20	21	22	23	24	25
26	27	28	29	30	31	

29
sunday

𝒜n Infinite Light shone on the earth on that first Christmas day,
and each year at this holy time the ether is filled with that Light.

—*Paramahansa Yogananda*

Aurora, Cantwell, Alaska   Photograph by Fred Hirschmann

$\mathcal{G}$lide through the skies of infinity,
attracting all beauty lovers toward the Most Beautiful.

—*Paramahansa Yogananda*

Sandhill crane, Bosque del Apache National Wildlife Refuge, New Mexico   Photograph by Arthur Morris/Jaynes Gallery/DanitaDelimont.com

December/January

30
monday

31
tuesday

New Year's Day   *New Moon* ●

1
wednesday

Day After New Year's Day (N.Z.)   *Bank Holiday (Scot.)*

2
thursday

3
friday

December

s	m	t	w	t	f	s
1	2	3	4	5	6	7
8	9	10	11	12	13	14
15	16	17	18	19	20	21
22	23	24	25	26	27	28
29	30	31				

All Climate / up
Furnace
Jan. 2014
Thurs.
23rd.
11:00 - 1:00

4
saturday

January 2014

s	m	t	w	t	f	s
			1	2	3	4
5	6	7	8	9	10	11
12	13	14	15	16	17	18
19	20	21	22	23	24	25
26	27	28	29	30	31	

Paramahansa Yogananda's Birthday

5
sunday

ACKNOWLEDGMENTS

We wish to express our sincere appreciation to the following photographers and agencies who contributed to this year's *Inner Reflections* engagement calendar. Following a contributor's name, in parentheses, is the month and a day of the week, or other description, where each photo appears.

AKM Images, Inc. (4/22)

AnimalsAnimals/Earth Scenes (1/28; 4/1; 4/8; 12/9)

Ellen Anon (7/8)

Jon Arnold Images (11/11)

Brian Bevan (4/1)

Biosphoto (9/23)

Russ Burden (10/21)

Larry Calof (4/22)

Mary Clark (12/9)

Mark Conlin (1/28)

Shaun Cunningham (2/11; 6/10)

DanitaDelimont.com/Jaynes' Gallery (11/11; 12/30)

Terry Donnelly (7/22; 12/16)

Thomas Dressler (12/2)

Guy Edwardes (4/29)

Julie Eggers (6/3)

Dennis Fast (3/18; 5/6; 6/24)

Tim Fitzharris (2/18)

D. Fleetham (4/8)

Dennis Frates (2/25; 3/25; 7/29; 8/26)

Adam Gibbs (1/7; 8/5; 8/12; 10/14)

Don Grall (5/20)

Mike Grandmaison (1/14)

Darrell Gulin/Science Faction (5/27)

Fred Hirschmann (12/23)

Burt Jones and Maurine Shimlock (3/11)

Klein & Hubert (9/23)

Warren Krupsaw (3/4; 7/15)

Tom Mackie (cover; 9/9)

Kevin McNeal (6/17; 9/30; 11/25)

Arthur Morris (12/30)

Charles Needle (1/21; 5/13)

Reed Nelson (10/28)

Koji Okada/JTB Photo (12/31/2012)

Photo Researchers, Inc. (7/1)

Superstock (12/31/2012; 5/27)

Rosanne Tackaberry (2/4)

Jan Vermeer (9/2; 11/4)

Bret Webster (7/1)

Dave Welling (8/19)

Michael Wheatley (9/16; 11/18)

Jane Wingate (10/7)

Craig Wood (4/15)

"THE IDEAL OF LOVE FOR GOD AND SERVICE TO HUMANITY FOUND FULL EXPRESSION IN THE LIFE OF PARAMAHANSA YOGANANDA....THOUGH THE MAJOR PART OF HIS LIFE WAS SPENT OUTSIDE INDIA, STILL HE TAKES HIS PLACE AMONG OUR GREAT SAINTS. HIS WORK CONTINUES TO GROW AND SHINE EVER MORE BRIGHTLY, DRAWING PEOPLE EVERYWHERE ON THE PATH OF THE PILGRIMAGE OF THE SPIRIT."

— *from a tribute by the Government of India upon issuing a special commemorative stamp in honor of*

PARAMAHANSA YOGANANDA
1893–1952

~

BORN IN NORTHERN INDIA IN 1893, Paramahansa Yogananda came to the United States in 1920 as a delegate to an international congress of religious leaders convening in Boston. He remained in the West for the better part of the next thirty-two years, until his passing in 1952. Reporting at that time on his life and work, a Los Angeles periodical wrote: "Yogananda made an outstanding cultural and spiritual contribution in furthering the cause of better understanding between East and West. He combined in a conspicuous degree the spiritual idealism of India with practical activity of the West....The centers he established, the great numbers he inspired to nobler living, and the ideals he planted in the common consciousness of humanity will ever remain a monument to his notable achievement."

Self-Realization Fellowship, the international nonprofit society founded by Paramahansa Yogananda in 1920, is dedicated to carrying on his spiritual and humanitarian work— fostering a spirit of greater harmony and understanding among those of all nations and faiths, and introducing to truth-seekers all over the world his universal teachings on the ancient science of Yoga.

Paramahansa Yogananda's life story, *Autobiography of a Yogi,* is considered a modern spiritual classic. It has been translated into more than twenty-five languages and is widely used in college and university courses. A perennial best seller since it was first published more than sixty years ago, the book has found its way into the hearts of readers around the world.

An introductory booklet about the life and teachings of Paramahansa Yogananda and a book catalog are available upon request.

SELF-REALIZATION FELLOWSHIP
3880 San Rafael Avenue • Los Angeles, California 90065-3219
Telephone (323) 225-2471 • Fax (323) 225-5088
www.yogananda-srf.org

BOOKS BY
PARAMAHANSA YOGANANDA

Available at bookstores or from our website:
http://bookstore.yogananda-srf.org

Autobiography of a Yogi

Autobiography of a Yogi *(Audiobook, read by Sir Ben Kingsley)*

The Science of Religion

The Law of Success

How You Can Talk With God

Metaphysical Meditations

Where There Is Light: *Insight and Inspiration for Meeting Life's Challenges*

The Yoga of Jesus: *Understanding the Hidden Teachings of the Gospels*

The Yoga of the Bhagavad Gita: *An Introduction to India's Universal Science of God-Realization*

THE COLLECTED TALKS AND ESSAYS
Volume I: Man's Eternal Quest
Volume II: The Divine Romance
Volume III: Journey to Self-realization

SELF-REALIZATION FELLOWSHIP LESSONS

The scientific techniques of meditation taught by Paramahansa Yogananda, including *Kriya Yoga* — as well as his guidance on all aspects of balanced spiritual living — are taught in the *Self-Realization Fellowship Lessons*. For further information, we welcome you to request ? the free booklet *Undreamed-of Possibilities.*

SELF-REALIZATION FELLOWSHIP
3880 San Rafael Avenue • Los Angeles, CA 90065-3219
TEL (323) 225-2471 • FAX (323) 225-5088
www.yogananda-srf.org

New Healthcare Law 10/1/13
" WASHINGTON Health ~~care~~ Plan Finder.com
~~#~~ Exchange # WA.St. -
Sign up by ~~#~~ 3/31/14 - closed enrollment til 10/2014.
Subsidies only available w/ the exchange (Greg)
~~Trump~~
St. Call Center - 855-923-4633

King County:

10-Things Policies MUST COVER ~~Fixit~~
HSA's + skinny catastrophic MAX Not qualify.

2012

January
s	m	t	w	t	f	s
1	2	3	4	5	6	7
8	9	10	11	12	13	14
15	16	17	18	19	20	21
22	23	24	25	26	27	28
29	30	31				

February
s	m	t	w	t	f	s
			1	2	3	4
5	6	7	8	9	10	11
12	13	14	15	16	17	18
19	20	21	22	23	24	25
26	27	28	29			

March
s	m	t	w	t	f	s
				1	2	3
4	5	6	7	8	9	10
11	12	13	14	15	16	17
18	19	20	21	22	23	24
25	26	27	28	29	30	31

April
s	m	t	w	t	f	s
1	2	3	4	5	6	7
8	9	10	11	12	13	14
15	16	17	18	19	20	21
22	23	24	25	26	27	28
29	30					

May
s	m	t	w	t	f	s
		1	2	3	4	5
6	7	8	9	10	11	12
13	14	15	16	17	18	19
20	21	22	23	24	25	26
27	28	29	30	31		

June
s	m	t	w	t	f	s
					1	2
3	4	5	6	7	8	9
10	11	12	13	14	15	16
17	18	19	20	21	22	23
24	25	26	27	28	29	30

July
s	m	t	w	t	f	s
1	2	3	4	5	6	7
8	9	10	11	12	13	14
15	16	17	18	19	20	21
22	23	24	25	26	27	28
29	30	31				

August
s	m	t	w	t	f	s
			1	2	3	4
5	6	7	8	9	10	11
12	13	14	15	16	17	18
19	20	21	22	23	24	25
26	27	28	29	30	31	

September
s	m	t	w	t	f	s
						1
2	3	4	5	6	7	8
9	10	11	12	13	14	15
16	17	18	19	20	21	22
23 30	24	25	26	27	28	29

October
s	m	t	w	t	f	s
	1	2	3	4	5	6
7	8	9	10	11	12	13
14	15	16	17	18	19	20
21	22	23	24	25	26	27
28	29	30	31			

November
s	m	t	w	t	f	s
				1	2	3
4	5	6	7	8	9	10
11	12	13	14	15	16	17
18	19	20	21	22	23	24
25	26	27	28	29	30	

December
s	m	t	w	t	f	s
						1
2	3	4	5	6	7	8
9	10	11	12	13	14	15
16	17	18	19	20	21	22
23 30	24 31	25	26	27	28	29

2014

January
s	m	t	w	t	f	s
			1	2	3	4
5	6	7	8	9	10	11
12	13	14	15	16	17	18
19	20	21	22	23	24	25
26	27	28	29	30	31	

February
s	m	t	w	t	f	s
						1
2	3	4	5	6	7	8
9	10	11	12	13	14	15
16	17	18	19	20	21	22
23	24	25	26	27	28	

March
s	m	t	w	t	f	s
						1
2	3	4	5	6	7	8
9	10	11	12	13	14	15
16	17	18	19	20	21	22
23 30	24 31	25	26	27	28	29

April
s	m	t	w	t	f	s
		1	2	3	4	5
6	7	8	9	10	11	12
13	14	15	16	17	18	19
20	21	22	23	24	25	26
27	28	29	30			

May
s	m	t	w	t	f	s
				1	2	3
4	5	6	7	8	9	10
11	12	13	14	15	16	17
18	19	20	21	22	23	24
25	26	27	28	29	30	31

June
s	m	t	w	t	f	s
1	2	3	4	5	6	7
8	9	10	11	12	13	14
15	16	17	18	19	20	21
22	23	24	25	26	27	28
29	30					

July
s	m	t	w	t	f	s
		1	2	3	4	5
6	7	8	9	10	11	12
13	14	15	16	17	18	19
20	21	22	23	24	25	26
27	28	29	30	31		

August
s	m	t	w	t	f	s
					1	2
3	4	5	6	7	8	9
10	11	12	13	14	15	16
17	18	19	20	21	22	23
24 31	25	26	27	28	29	30

September
s	m	t	w	t	f	s
	1	2	3	4	5	6
7	8	9	10	11	12	13
14	15	16	17	18	19	20
21	22	23	24	25	26	27
28	29	30				

October
s	m	t	w	t	f	s
			1	2	3	4
5	6	7	8	9	10	11
12	13	14	15	16	17	18
19	20	21	22	23	24	25
26	27	28	29	30	31	

November
s	m	t	w	t	f	s
						1
2	3	4	5	6	7	8
9	10	11	12	13	14	15
16	17	18	19	20	21	22
23 30	24	25	26	27	28	29

December
s	m	t	w	t	f	s
	1	2	3	4	5	6
7	8	9	10	11	12	13
14	15	16	17	18	19	20
21	22	23	24	25	26	27
28	29	30	31			

2013

January
s	m	t	w	t	f	s
		1	2	3	4	5
6	7	8	9	10	11	12
13	14	15	16	17	18	19
20	21	22	23	24	25	26
27	28	29	30	31		

February
s	m	t	w	t	f	s
					1	2
3	4	5	6	7	8	9
10	11	12	13	14	15	16
17	18	19	20	21	22	23
24	25	26	27	28		

March
s	m	t	w	t	f	s
					1	2
3	4	5	6	7	8	9
10	11	12	13	14	15	16
17	18	19	20	21	22	23
24 31	25	26	27	28	29	30

April
s	m	t	w	t	f	s
	1	2	3	4	5	6
7	8	9	10	11	12	13
14	15	16	17	18	19	20
21	22	23	24	25	26	27
28	29	30				

May
s	m	t	w	t	f	s
			1	2	3	4
5	6	7	8	9	10	11
12	13	14	15	16	17	18
19	20	21	22	23	24	25
26	27	28	29	30	31	

June
s	m	t	w	t	f	s
						1
2	3	4	5	6	7	8
9	10	11	12	13	14	15
16	17	18	19	20	21	22
23 30	24	25	26	27	28	29

July
s	m	t	w	t	f	s
	1	2	3	4	5	6
7	8	9	10	11	12	13
14	15	16	17	18	19	20
21	22	23	24	25	26	27
28	29	30	31			

August
s	m	t	w	t	f	s
				1	2	3
4	5	6	7	8	9	10
11	12	13	14	15	16	17
18	19	20	21	22	23	24
25	26	27	28	29	30	31

September
s	m	t	w	t	f	s
1	2	3	4	5	6	7
8	9	10	11	12	13	14
15	16	17	18	19	20	21
22	23	24	25	26	27	28
29	30					

October
s	m	t	w	t	f	s
	1	2	3	4	5	
6	7	8	9	10	11	12
13	14	15	16	17	18	19
20	21	22	23	24	25	26
27	28	29	30	31		

November
s	m	t	w	t	f	s
					1	2
3	4	5	6	7	8	9
10	11	12	13	14	15	16
17	18	19	20	21	22	23
24	25	26	27	28	29	30

December
s	m	t	w	t	f	s
1	2	3	4	5	6	7
8	9	10	11	12	13	14
15	16	17	18	19	20	21
22	23	24	25	26	27	28
29	30	31				

January

Sunday	Monday	Tuesday	Wednesday	Thursday	Friday	Saturday
		1	2	3	4	5
6	7	8	9	10	11	12
13	14	15	16	17	18	19
20	21	22	23	24	25	26
27	28	29	30	31		

Jan 1   New Year's Day

Jan 2   Day after New Year's Day (N.Z.)
             Bank Holiday (Scotland)

Jan 5   Paramahansa Yogananda's Birthday

Jan 21   Martin Luther King, Jr's Birthday
             (Observed)

Jan 26   Australia Day (Aus.)

February

Sunday	Monday	Tuesday	Wednesday	Thursday	Friday	Saturday
					1	2
3	4	5	6	7	8	9
10	11	12	13	14	15	16
17	18	19	20	21	22	23
24	25	26	27	28		

Feb 6   Waitangi Day (N.Z.)
Feb 12   Lincoln's Birthday
Feb 14   St. Valentine's Day
Feb 18   Presidents' Day (Observed)
Feb 22   Washington's Birthday

March

Sunday	Monday	Tuesday	Wednesday	Thursday	Friday	Saturday
					1	2
3	4	5	6	7	8	9
10	11	12	13	14	15	16
17	18	19	20	21	22	23
24	25	26	27	28	29	30
31						

Mar 1   St. David's Day (Wales)
Mar 7   Paramahansa Yogananda's Mahasamadhi
Mar 9   Sri Yukteswar's Mahasamadhi

Mar 10   Daylight Saving Time Begins (U.S. & Canada)
           Mothering Sunday (England)
Mar 17   St. Patrick's Day
Mar 20   Vernal Equinox

Mar 26   Passover Begins
Mar 29   Good Friday
Mar 31   Daylight Savings Time Begins (U.K. & European Union)
           Easter Sunday

April

Sunday	Monday	Tuesday	Wednesday	Thursday	Friday	Saturday
	1	2	3	4	5	6
7	8	9	10	11	12	13
14	15	16	17	18	19	20
21	22	23	24	25	26	27
28	29	30				

Apr 1   Easter Monday (All except U.S. & Scotland)
Apr 22   Earth Day
Apr 23   St. George's Day (England)
Apr 25   ANZAC Day (N.Z./Australia)

May

Sunday	Monday	Tuesday	Wednesday	Thursday	Friday	Saturday
			1	2	3	4
5	6	7	8	9	10	11
12	13	14	15	16	17	18
19	20	21	22	23	24	25
26	27	28	29	30	31	

May 2   National Day of Prayer

May 6   May Day Bank Holiday (U.K. & Scotland)

May 10 Sri Yukteswar's birthday

May 12 Mother's Day
         (U.S., Canada, Australia & N.Z.)

May 20 Victoria Day (Canada)

May 27 Memorial Day

May 27 Spring Bank Holiday (U.K. & Scotland)

June

Sunday	Monday	Tuesday	Wednesday	Thursday	Friday	Saturday
						1
2	3	4	5	6	7	8
9	10	11	12	13	14	15
16	17	18	19	20	21	22
23	24	25	26	27	28	29
30						

Jun 3   Queen's Birthday (N.Z.)
Jun 10   Queen's Birthday (Australia)
Jun 16   Father's Day (U.S., Canada & U.K.)
Jun 21   Summer Solstice

July

Sunday	Monday	Tuesday	Wednesday	Thursday	Friday	Saturday
	1	2	3	4	5	6
7	8	9	10	11	12	13
14	15	16	17	18	19	20
21	22	23	24	25	26	27
28	29	30	31			

Jul 1   Canada Day (Canada)

Jul 4   Independence Day

Jul 25   Mahavatar Babaji Commemoration Day

August

Sunday	Monday	Tuesday	Wednesday	Thursday	Friday	Saturday
				1	2	3
4	5	6	7	8	9	10
11	12	13	14	15	16	17
18	19	20	21	22	23	24
25	26	27	28	29	30	31

Aug 26 Summer Bank Holiday (U.K. & Scotland)
Aug 28 Janmashtami

September

Sunday	Monday	Tuesday	Wednesday	Thursday	Friday	Saturday
1	2	3	4	5	6	7
8	9	10	11	12	13	14
15	16	17	18	19	20	21
22	23	24	25	26	27	28
29	30					

Sep 1   Father's Day (Australia & N.Z.)

Sep 2   Labor Day (U.S. & Canada)

Sep 5   Rosh Hashanah

Sep 14 Yom Kippur

Sep 21 U.N. International Day of Peace

Sep 22 Autumnal Equinox

Sep 26 Lahiri Mahasaya's Mahasamadhi

Sep 30 Lahiri Mahasaya's Birthday

October

Sunday	Monday	Tuesday	Wednesday	Thursday	Friday	Saturday
		1	2	3	4	5
6	7	8	9	10	11	12
13	14	15	16	17	18	19
20	21	22	23	24	25	26
27	28	29	30	31		

Oct 14 Columbus Day
        Thanksgiving Day (Canada)
Oct 27 Daylight Saving Time Ends (U.K. & European Union)
Oct 28 Labour Day (N.Z.)
Oct 31 Halloween (U.S., Canada, & U.K.)

November

Sunday	Monday	Tuesday	Wednesday	Thursday	Friday	Saturday
					1	2
3	4	5	6	7	8	9
10	11	12	13	14	15	16
17	18	19	20	21	22	23
24	25	26	27	28	29	30

Nov 3   Daylight Saving Time Ends
        (U.S. & Canada)

Nov 5   Guy Fawkes Day (England)

Nov 5   General Election Day

Nov 10 Remembrance Sunday (U.K.)

Nov 11 Veterans' Day
        Remembrance Day (Canada)

Nov 28 Thanksgiving Day

Nov 27 Hanukkah

December

Sunday	Monday	Tuesday	Wednesday	Thursday	Friday	Saturday
1	2	3	4	5	6	7
8	9	10	11	12	13	14
15	16	17	18	19	20	21
22	23	24	25	26	27	28
29	30	31				

Dec 2   St. Andrew's Day (Scotland – Observed)
Dec 21 Winter Solstice
Dec 25 Christmas
Dec 26 Boxing Day (Canada, U.K., Australia, N.Z.)

Garage Door Info:
 DisTRibudOORS - doors & openers
 206 - 443 - 1640

To determine how many Tsps of sugar
in food - take 1. Carbohydrate gram TOT.
Subtract 2. Fiber Grams, 3. Then divide
by 5. — 8 Tsps a day enough. (or 16?)